KAISER CHIEFS
"OFF WITH THEIR HEADS"

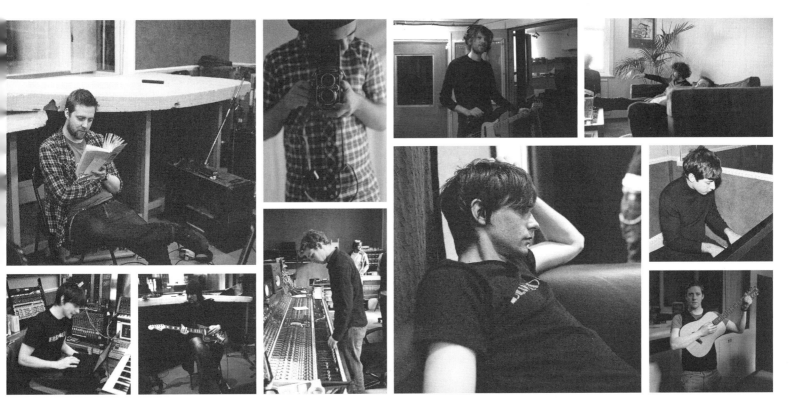

Wise Publications
part of The Music Sales Group

London / New York / Paris / Sydney / Copenhagen / Berlin / Madrid / Tokyo

Published by
Wise Publications
14-15 Berners Street, London W1T 3LJ, UK.

Exclusive distributors:
Music Sales Limited
Distribution Centre, Newmarket Road,
Bury St Edmunds, Suffolk, IP33 3YB, UK.

Music Sales Pty Limited
20 Resolution Drive, Caringbah, NSW 2229, Australia.

Order No. AM996127
ISBN 978-1-84772-857-9

Music arranged by Matt Cowe.
Music processed by Paul Ewers Music Design.
Edited by Tom Farncombe.

Printed in the EU.

GUITAR TABLATURE EXPLAINED

Guitar music can be notated in three different ways: on a musical stave, in tablature, and in rhythm slashes.

RHYTHM SLASHES: are written above the stave. Strum chords in the rhythm indicated. Round noteheads indicate single notes.

THE MUSICAL STAVE: shows pitches and rhythms and is divided by lines into bars. Pitches are named after the first seven letters of the alphabet.

TABLATURE: graphically represents the guitar fingerboard. Each horizontal line represents a string, and each number represents a fret.

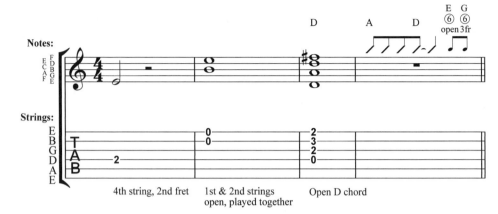

4th string, 2nd fret   1st & 2nd strings open, played together   Open D chord

DEFINITIONS FOR SPECIAL GUITAR NOTATION

SEMI-TONE BEND: Strike the note and bend up a semi-tone (½ step).

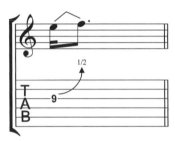

BEND & RELEASE: Strike the note and bend up as indicated, then release back to the original note.

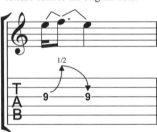

HAMMER-ON: Strike the first note with one finger, then sound the second note (on the same string) with another finger by fretting it without picking.

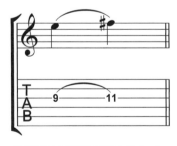

NATURAL HARMONIC: Strike the note while the fret-hand lightly touches the string directly over the fret indicated.

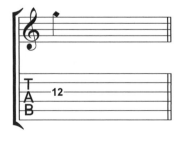

WHOLE-TONE BEND: Strike the note and bend up a whole-tone (full step).

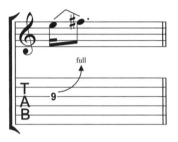

COMPOUND BEND & RELEASE: Strike the note and bend up and down in the rhythm indicated.

PULL-OFF: Place both fingers on the note to be sounded, strike the first note and without picking, pull the finger off to sound the second note.

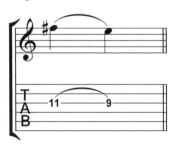

PICK SCRAPE: The edge of the pick is rubbed down (or up) the string, producing a scratchy sound.

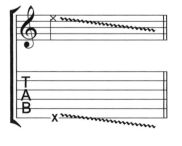

GRACE NOTE BEND: Strike the note and bend as indicated. Play the first note as quickly as possible.

PRE-BEND: Bend the note as indicated, then strike it.

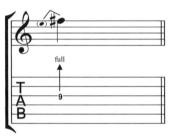

LEGATO SLIDE (GLISS): Strike the first note and then slide the same fret-hand finger up or down to the second note. The second note is not struck.

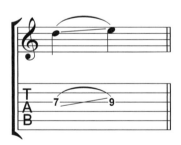

PALM MUTING: The note is partially muted by the pick hand lightly touching the string(s) just before the bridge.

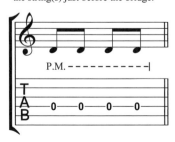

QUARTER-TONE BEND: Strike the note and bend up a ¼ step

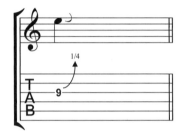

PRE-BEND & RELEASE: Bend the note as indicated. Strike it and release the note back to the original pitch.

MUFFLED STRINGS: A percussive sound is produced by laying the first hand across the string(s) without depressing, and striking them with the pick hand.

SHIFT SLIDE (GLISS & RESTRIKE) Same as legato slide, except the second note is struck.

TAP HARMONIC: The note is fretted normally and a harmonic is produced by tapping or slapping the fret indicated in brackets (which will be twelve frets higher than the fretted note.)

TAPPING: Hammer ('tap') the fret indicated with the pick-hand index or middle finger and pull-off to the note fretted by the fret hand.

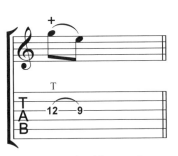

PINCH HARMONIC: The note is fretted normally and a harmonic is produced by adding the edge of the thumb or the tip of the index finger of the pick hand to the normal pick attack.

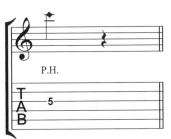

ARTIFICIAL HARMONIC: The note fretted normally and a harmonic is produced by gently resting the pick hand's index finger directly above the indicated fret (in brackets) while plucking the appropriate string.

TRILL: Very rapidly alternate between the notes indicated by continuously hammering-on and pulling-off.

RAKE: Drag the pick across the strings with a single motion.

TREMOLO PICKING: The note is picked as rapidly and continously as possible.

ARPEGGIATE: Play the notes of the chord indicated by quickly rolling them from bottom to top.

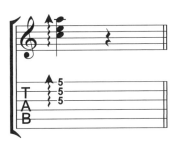

SWEEP PICKING: Rhythmic downstroke and/or upstroke motion across the strings.

VIBRATO DIVE BAR AND RETURN: The pitch of the note or chord is dropped a specific number of steps (in rhythm) then returned to the original pitch.

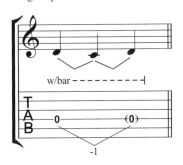

VIBRATO BAR SCOOP: Depress the bar just before striking the note, then quickly release the bar.

VIBRATO BAR DIP: Strike the note and then immediately drop a specific number of steps, then release back to the original pitch.

ADDITIONAL MUSICAL DEFINITIONS

 (accent) Accentuate note (play it louder)

 (accent) Accentuate note with greater intensity

 (staccato) Shorten time value of note

⊓   Downstroke

V   Upstroke

D.S. al Coda

D.C. al Fine

tacet

Go back to the sign (%), then play until the bar marked ***To Coda*** ⊕ then skip to the section marked ⊕ *Coda*

Go back to the beginning of the song and play until the bar marked ***Fine.***

Instrument is silent (drops out).

Repeat bars between signs

1. **2.**

When a repeat section has different endings, play the first ending only the first time and the second ending only the second time.

NOTE: Tablature numbers in brackets mean:
1. The note is sustained, but a new articulation (such as hammer-on or slide) begins
2. A note may be fretted but not necessarily played.

SPANISH METAL

Words & Music by
Charlie Wilson, Nicholas Hodgson, Andrew White, James Rix & Nicholas Baines

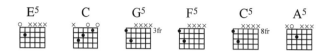

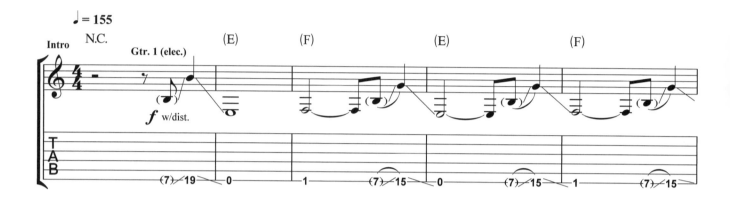

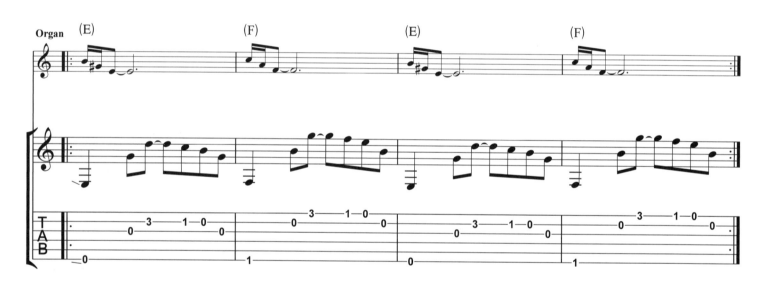

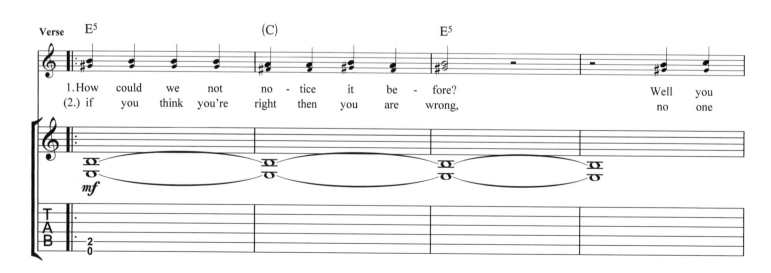

1. How could we not notice it be - fore? Well you
(2.) if you think you're right then you are wrong, no one

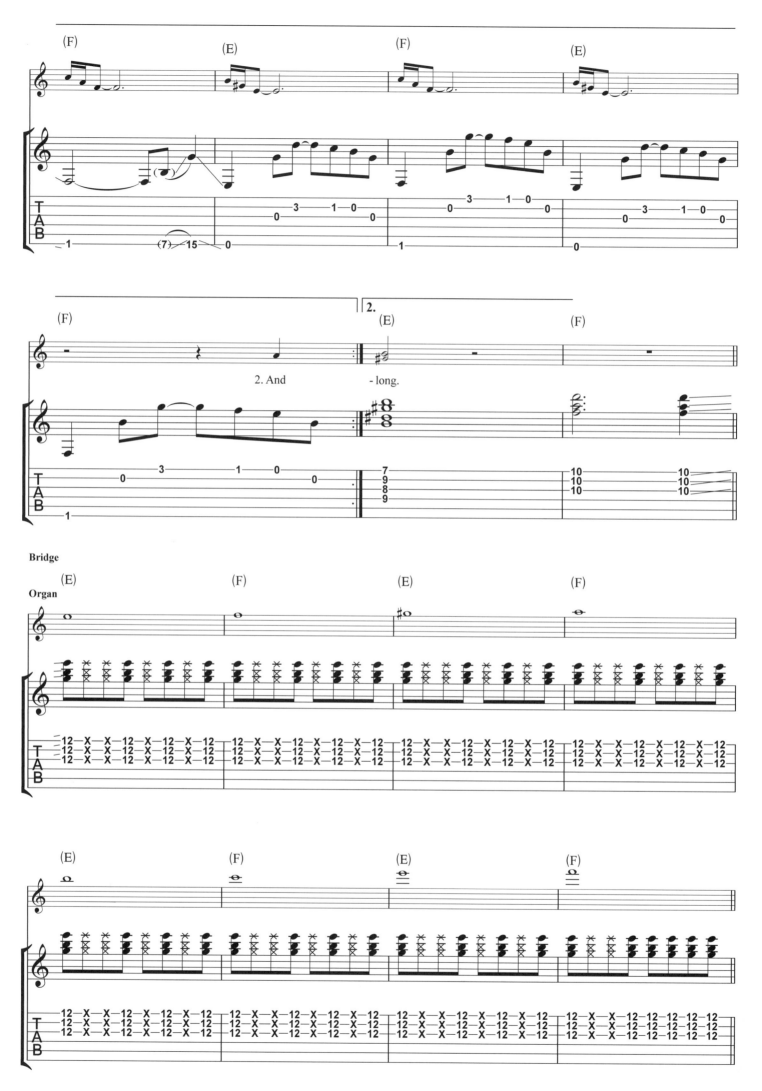

Bridge

Organ

Chorus

The pen-ny drops from the top of Tour Eif-fel,
A pen-ny more through the floor of Sa-cre Coeur,
Through the bou-le-
from the Spa-nish

-vards to Taj Ma-hal.
Mane to the York-shire moors.

Let ring…

1.

2.

9

NEVER MISS A BEAT

Words & Music by
Charlie Wilson, Nicholas Hodgson, Andrew White, James Rix & Nicholas Baines

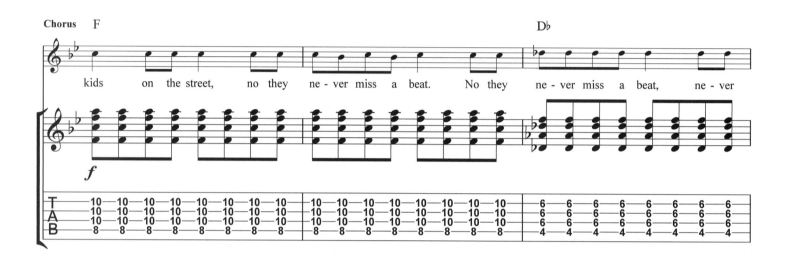

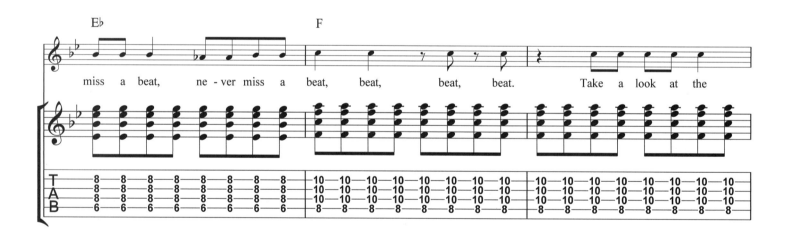

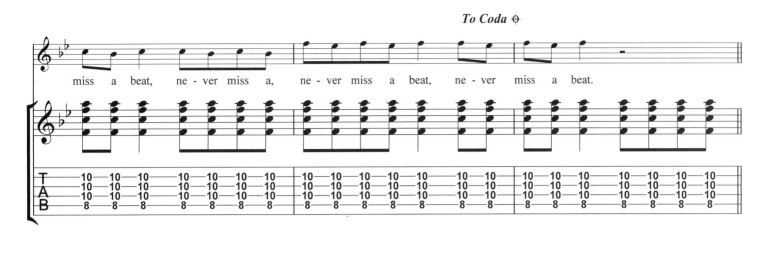

miss a beat, ne - ver miss a, ne - ver miss a beat, ne - ver miss a beat.

Interlude (G⁵)

mf

D.S. al Coda

⊕ *Coda*

F

Interlude

(G⁵)

miss a beat.

f

Bass arr. for Gtr.

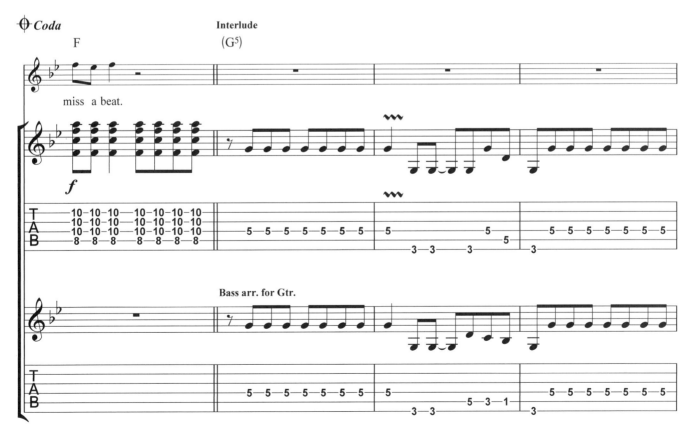

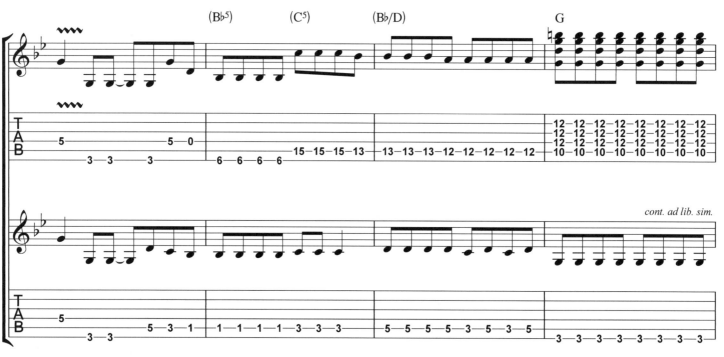

Take a look, take a look, take a look at the

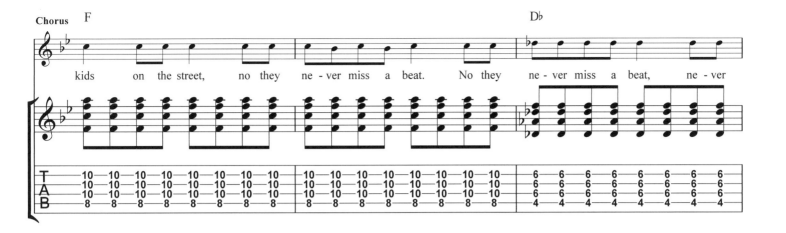

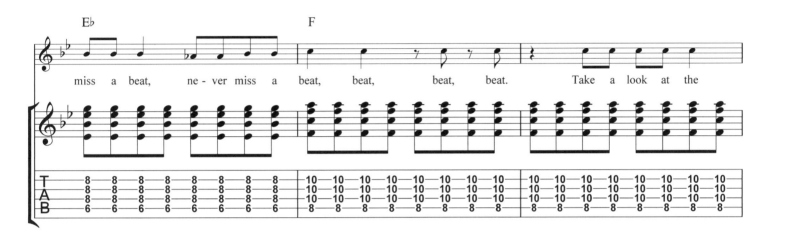

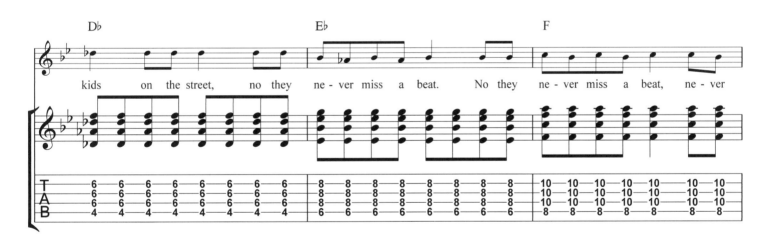

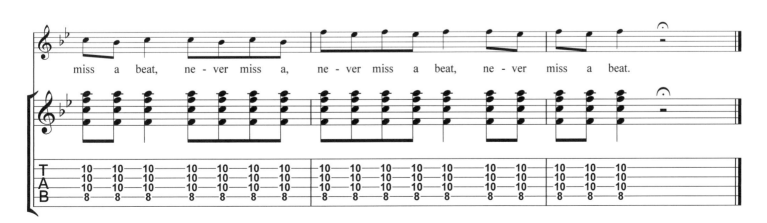

LIKE IT TOO MUCH

Words & Music by
Charlie Wilson, Nicholas Hodgson, Andrew White, James Rix & Nicholas Baines

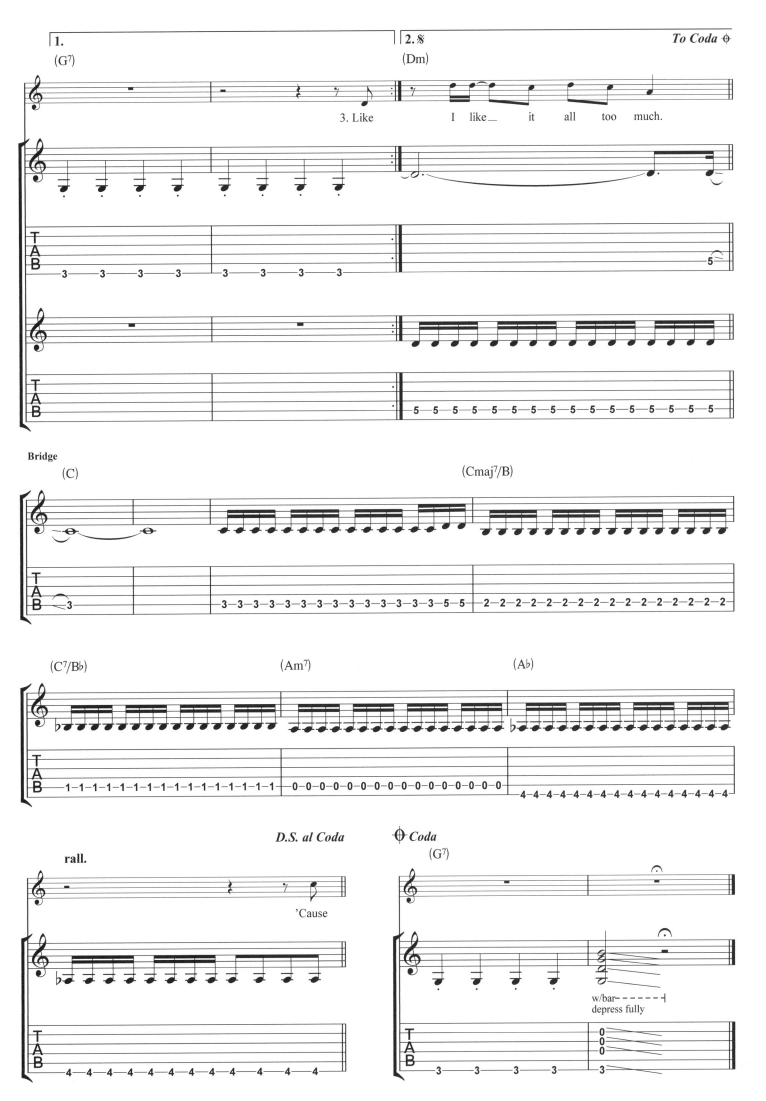

YOU WANT HISTORY

Words & Music by
Charlie Wilson, Nicholas Hodgson, Andrew White, James Rix & Nicholas Baines

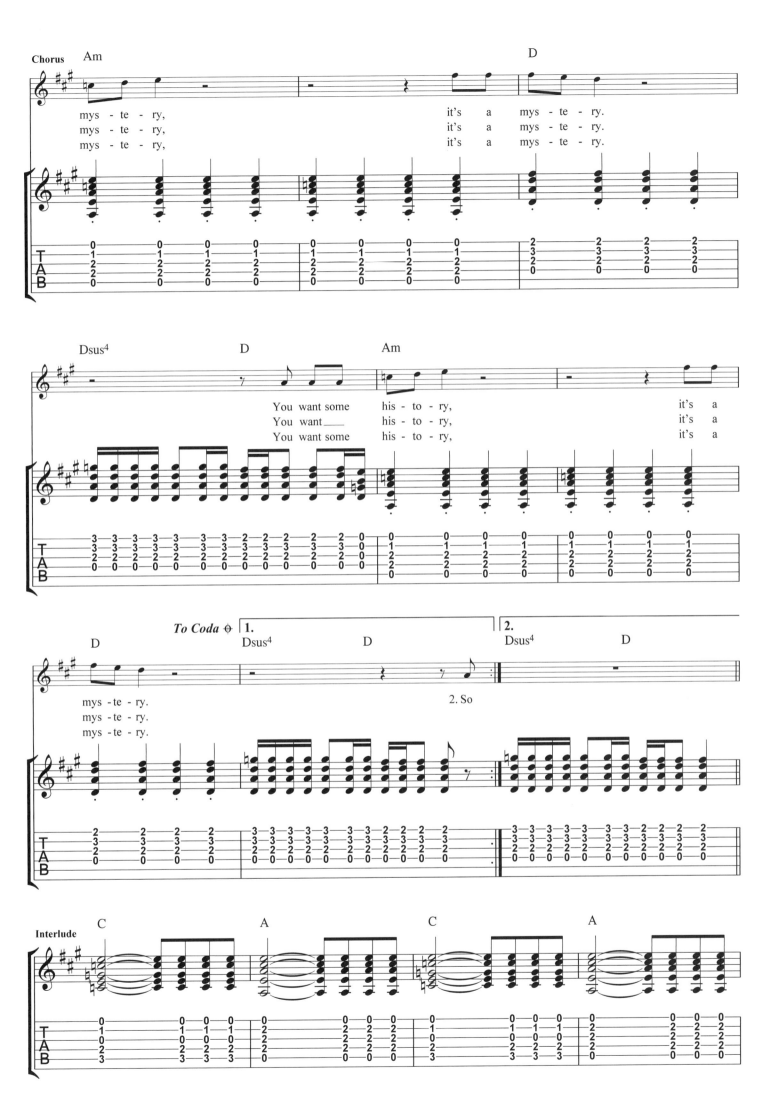

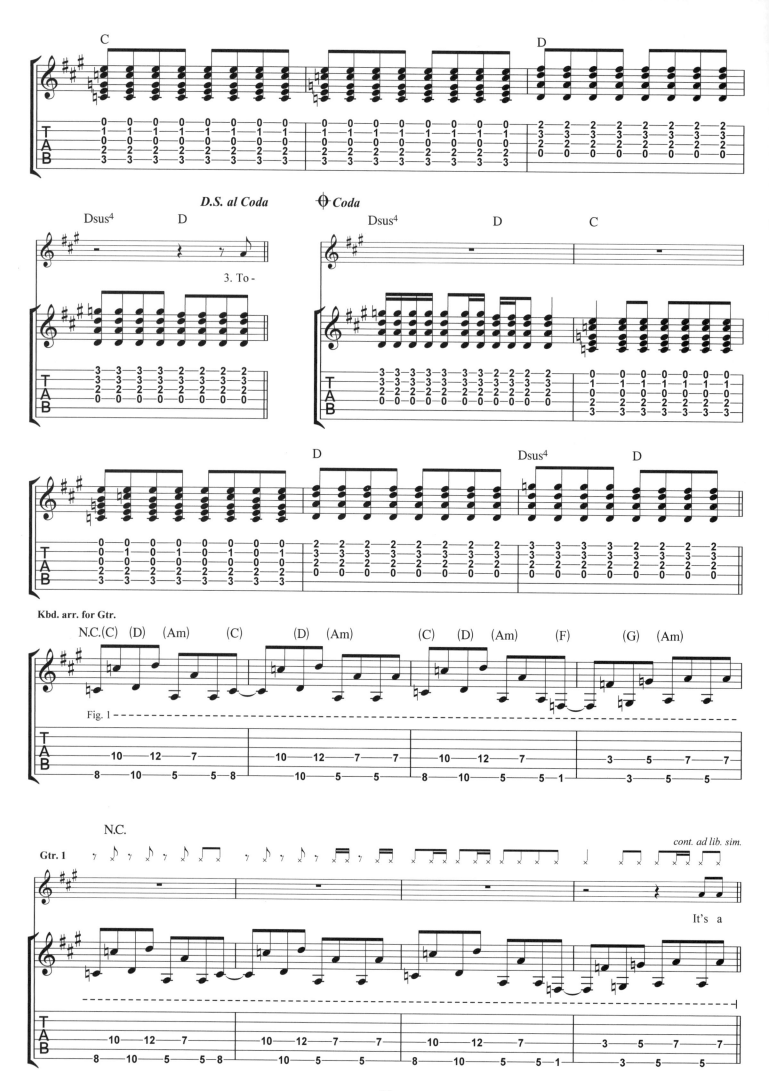

D.S. al Coda $\oplus$ *Coda*

Kbd. arr. for Gtr.

Gtr. 1

CAN'T SAY WHAT I MEAN

Words & Music by
Charlie Wilson, Nicholas Hodgson, Andrew White, James Rix & Nicholas Baines

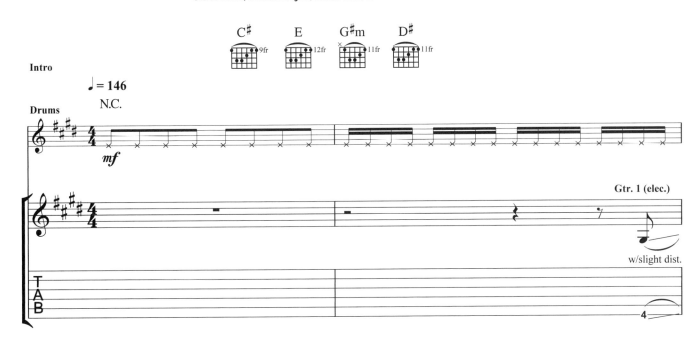

no - thing I say's so im - por - tant that it can't be short - ened to fit on a badge._____ I

wish that I could be con - trite and del - i - ver her sound - bites, but here is the catch.___ I can't say what I mean.___

26

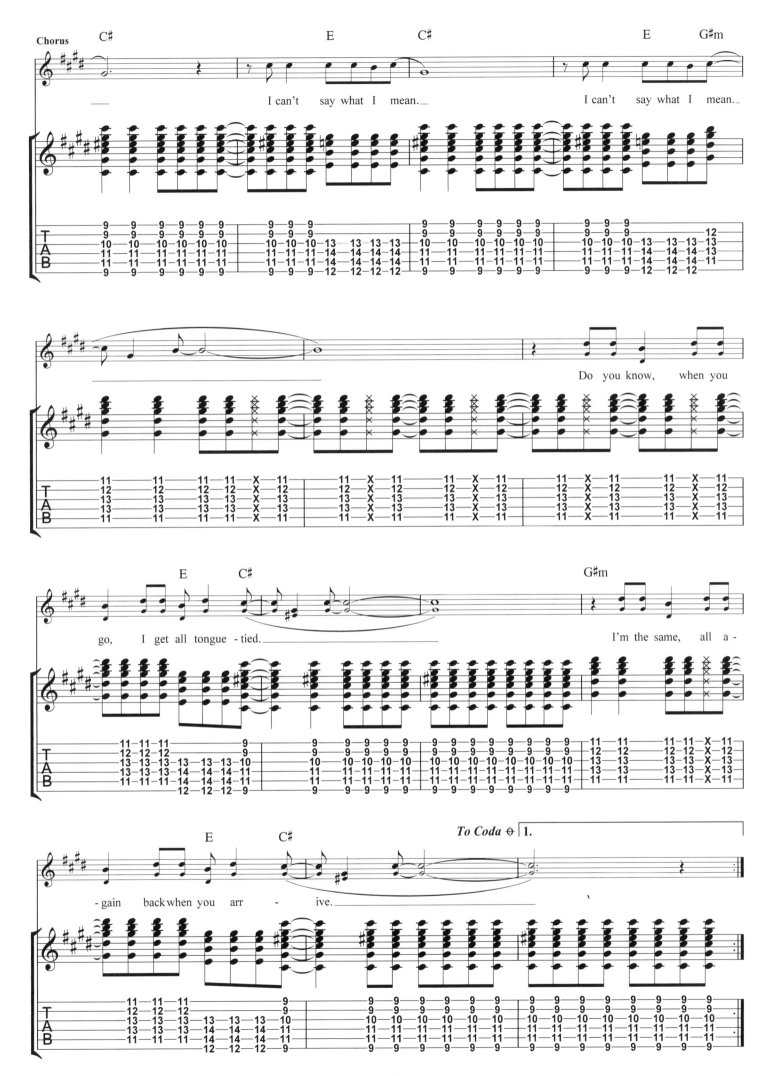

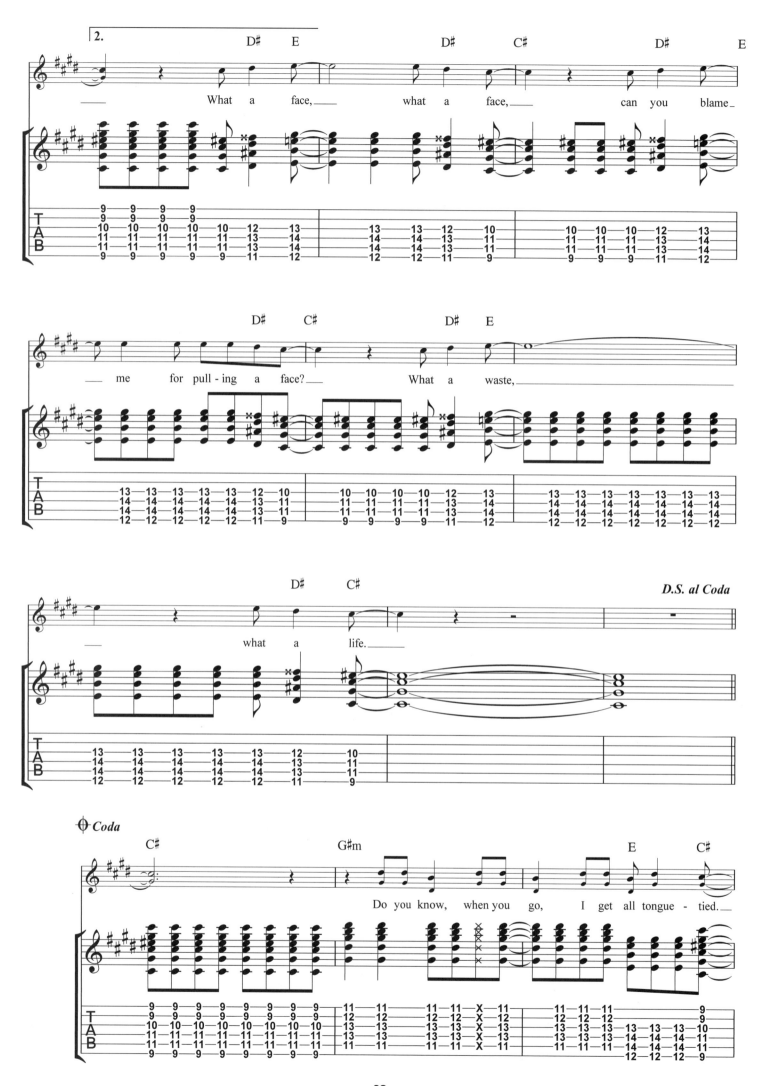

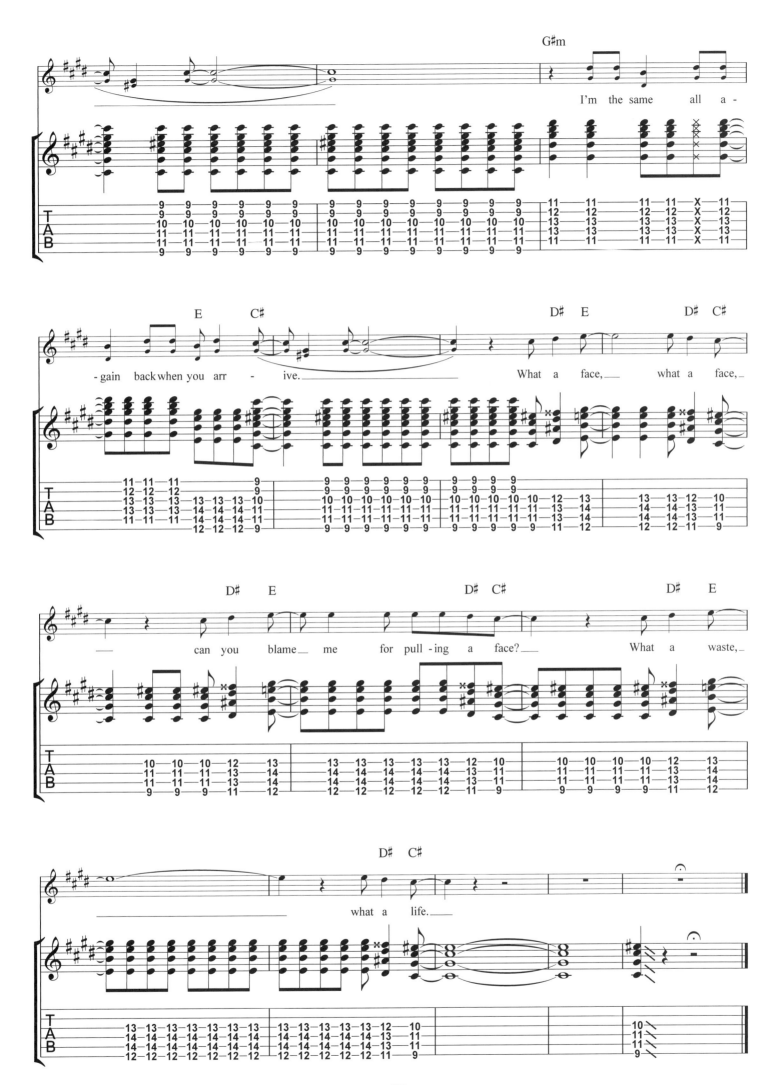

GOOD DAYS BAD DAYS

Words & Music by
Charlie Wilson, Nicholas Hodgson, Andrew White, James Rix & Nicholas Baines

Hey, hey. Hey, hey.

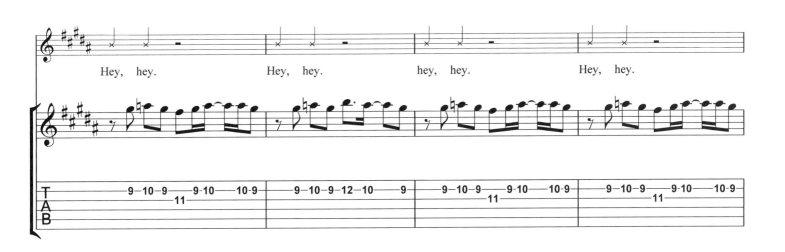

Hey, hey. Hey, hey. hey, hey. Hey, hey.

Hey, hey. Hey, hey. (He's get-ting a-way with it.) If you had a diff'rent at-ti-tude

in-stead of take and take and take, you have missed an op-por-tu - ni-ty   and that's a real - ly big_ mis-take.

F#m

If you had a diff-'rent at - ti-tude,   you'd still have good   days_   and bad   days._____

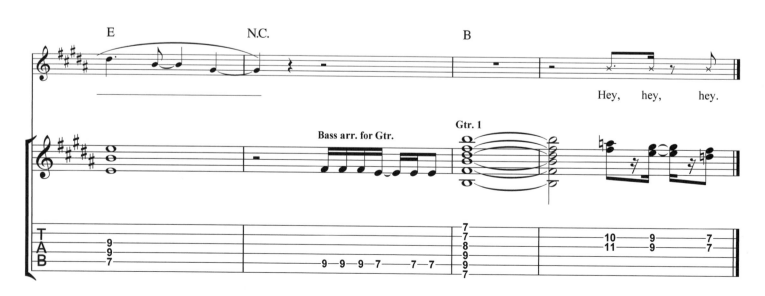

E   N.C.   B

Hey,   hey,   hey.

Bass arr. for Gtr.   Gtr. 1

TOMATO IN THE RAIN

Words & Music by
Charlie Wilson, Nicholas Hodgson, Andrew White, James Rix & Nicholas Baines

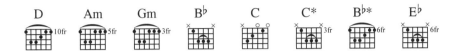

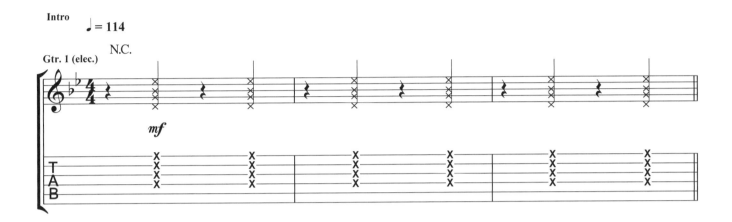

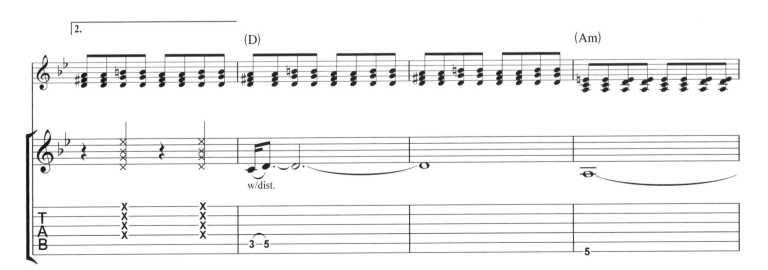

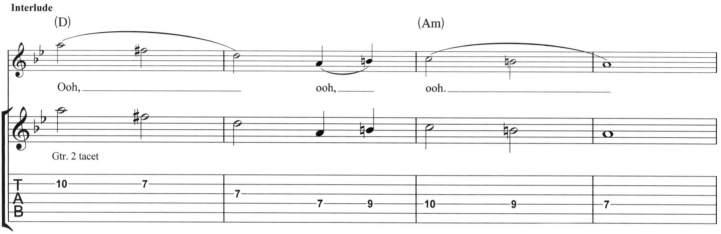

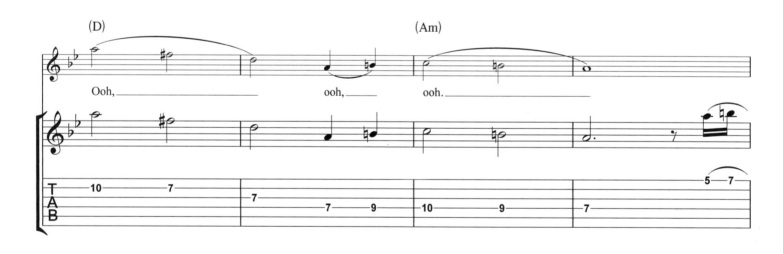

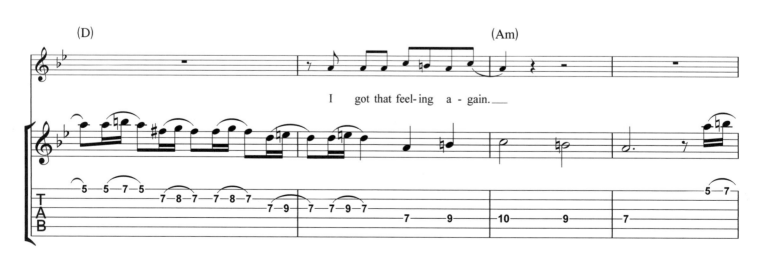

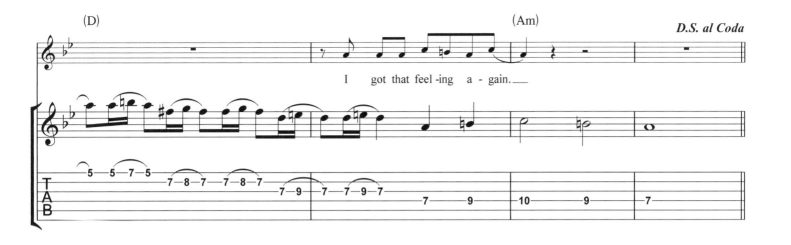

I got that feel-ing a - gain.___

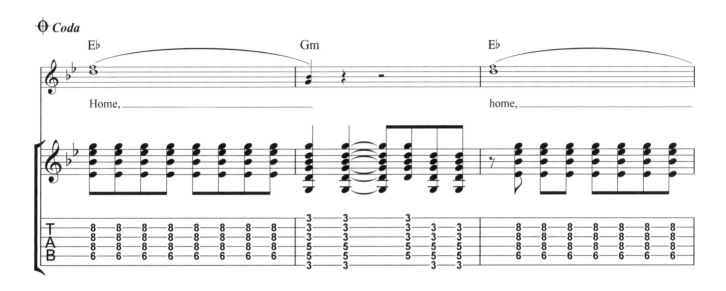

Home,_____ home,_____

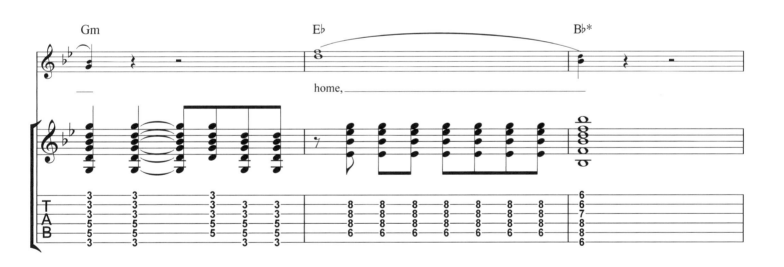

home,_____

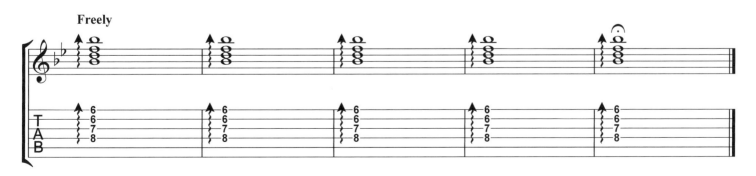

HALF THE TRUTH

Words & Music by
Charlie Wilson, Nicholas Hodgson, Andrew White, James Rix & Nicholas Baines

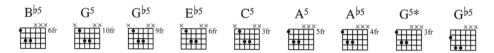

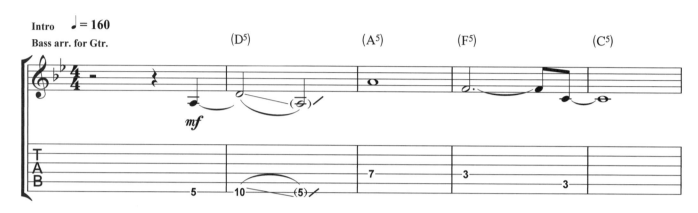

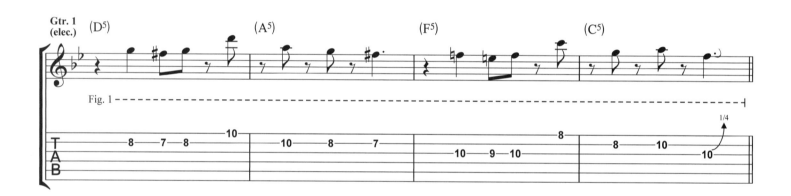

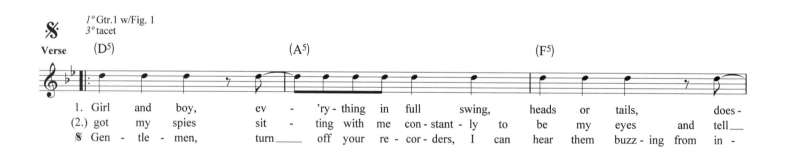

1. Girl and boy, ev'ry-thing in full swing, heads or tails, does-
(2.) got my spies sit-ting with me con-stant-ly to be my eyes and tell

% Gen-tle-men, turn off your re-cor-ders, I can hear them buzz-ing from in-

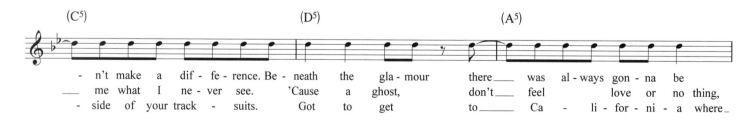

- n't make a dif-fe-rence. Be-neath the gla-mour there was al-ways gon-na be
  me what I ne-ver see. 'Cause a ghost, don't feel love or no thing,
- side of your track-suits. Got to get to Ca-li-for-ni-a where

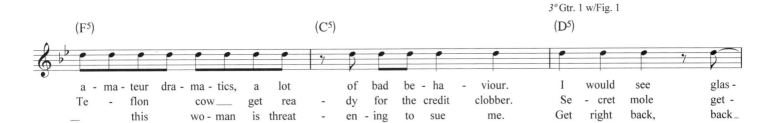

(F5) (C5) (D5)

a - ma - teur dra - ma - tics, a lot of bad be - ha - viour. I would see glas -
Te - flon cow — get rea - dy for the credit clobber. Se - cret mole get -
— this wo - man is threat - en - ing to sue me. Get right back, back —

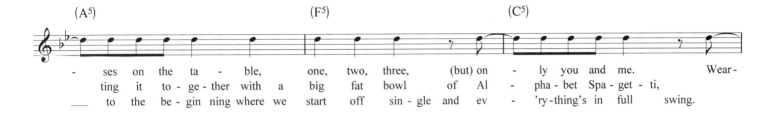

(A5) (F5) (C5)

- ses on the ta - ble, one, two, three, (but) on - ly you and me. Wear -
ting it to - ge - ther with a big fat bowl of Al - pha - bet Spa - get - ti,
— to the be - gin - ning where we start off sin - gle and ev - 'ry - thing's in full swing.

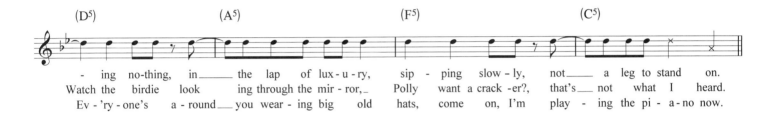

(D5) (A5) (F5) (C5)

- ing no - thing, in — the lap of lux - u - ry, sip - ping slow - ly, not — a leg to stand on.
Watch the birdie look - ing through the mir - ror, — Polly want a crack - er?, that's — not what I heard.
Ev - 'ry - one's a - round — you wear - ing big old hats, come on, I'm play - ing the pi - a - no now.

Pre chorus

Bb5

Take my — mo - ney, — it's a waste of —

Bb5

pa - per, — leave the — ta - ble, —

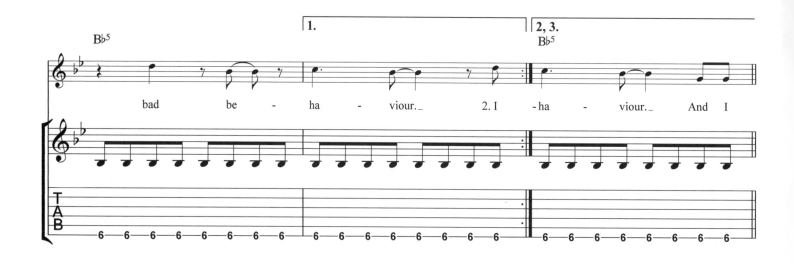

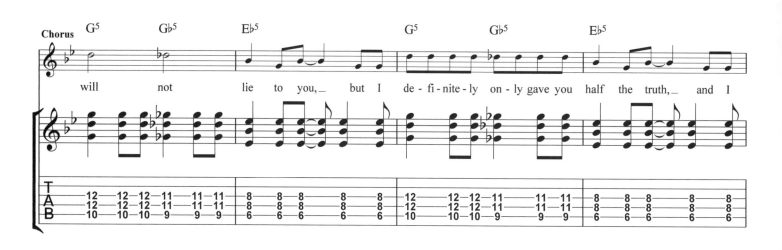

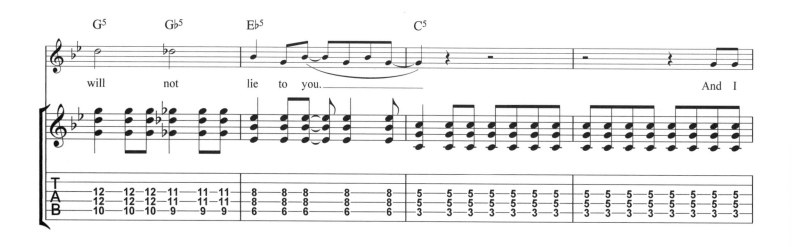

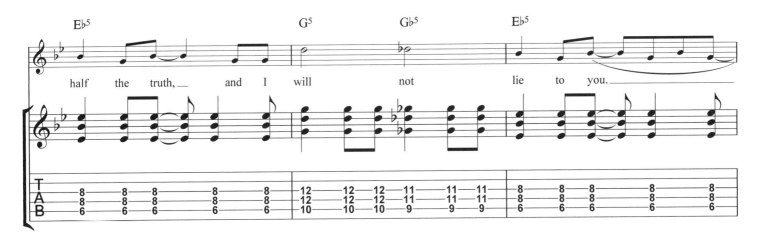

half the truth, ___ and I will not lie to you. ___

To Coda ⊕

D.S. al Coda

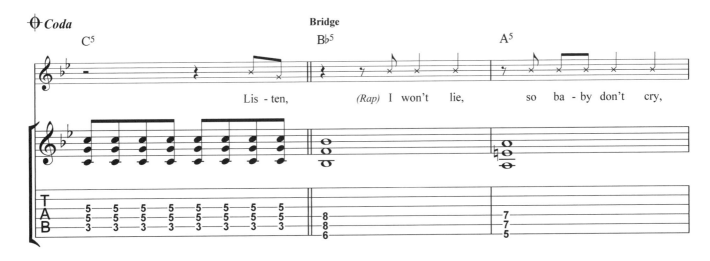

⊕ *Coda*

Bridge

Lis - ten, (Rap) I won't lie, so ba - by don't cry,

the way I'm feel - in' right now, I'm feel - in' so high. I can't tell you the truth,

44

ALWAYS HAPPENS LIKE THAT

Words & Music by
Charlie Wilson, Nicholas Hodgson, Andrew White, James Rix & Nicholas Baines

ADDICTED TO DRUGS

Words & Music by
Charlie Wilson, Nicholas Hodgson, Andrew White, James Rix & Nicholas Baines

REMEMBER YOU'RE A GIRL

Words & Music by
Charlie Wilson, Nicholas Hodgson, Andrew White, James Rix & Nicholas Baines

Intro

♩ = 114

Gtrs. 1+2 (elec.)
composite part

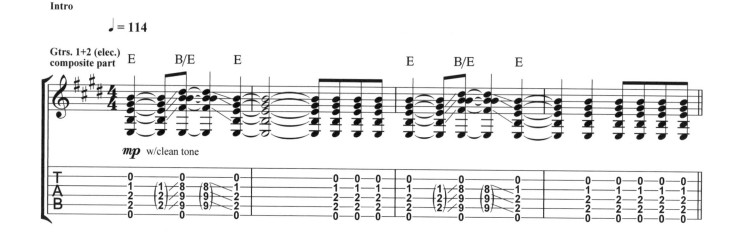

mp w/clean tone

2° Gtr. 3

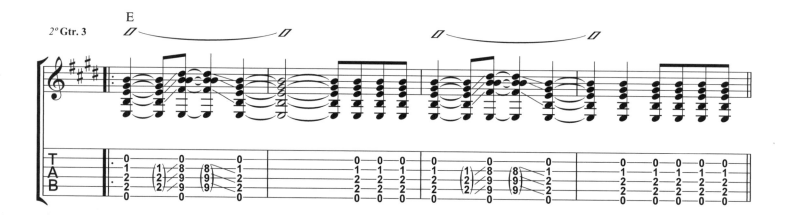

Verse

1. Pick the one___ you like,___ love the one___ you're with.___ You're
2.(It's)time to run___ a race,___ we're all on___ the way.___ You're

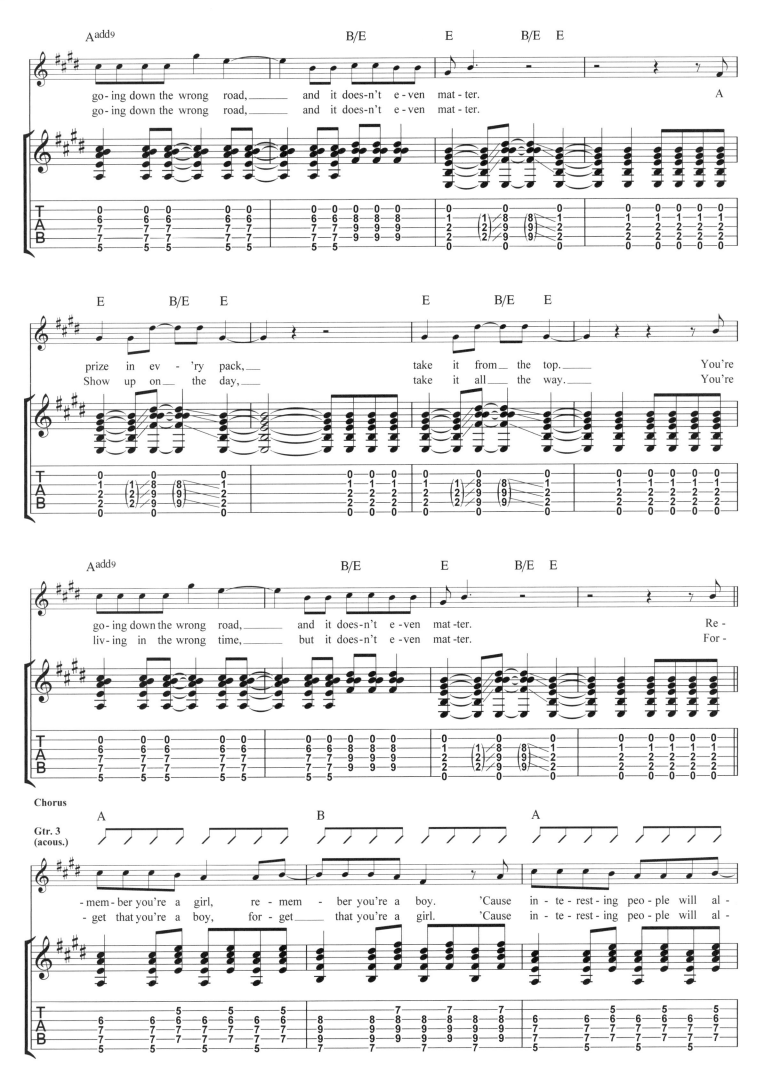

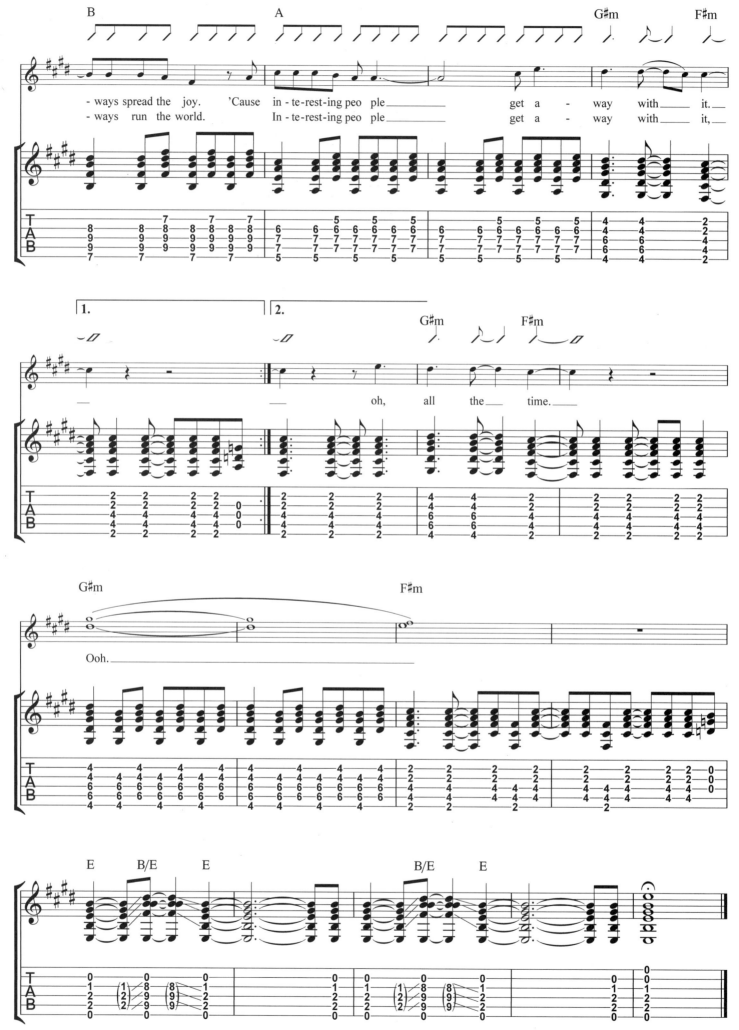